THE BOSS

A DAVID FICKLING BOOK 978 0857 56026 1

This edition published in Great Britain in 2011 by David Fickling Books,
a division of Random House Children's Books
A Random House Group Company

1 3 5 7 9 10 8 6 4 2

Text copyright © John Aggs 2011
Illustrations copyright © Patrice Aggs 2011

DAVID FICKLING BOOKS
31 Beaumont Street, Oxford, OX1 2NP

www.**kids**at**randomhouse**.co.uk
www.totally**randombooks**.co.uk

Addresses for companies within
The Random House Group Limited can be found at:
www.randomhouse.co.uk/offices.htm

THE RANDOM HOUSE GROUP Limited Reg. No. 954009

A CIP catalogue record for this book is available from the
British Library.

Printed and bound in China

THE BOSS

STORY
JOHN AGGS

ART
PATRICE AGGS

David Fickling Books
OXFORD · NEW YORK

BO-R-R-R-R-ING!

OH, NAZIM, STOP WHINING. IT'S NOT *THAT* BAD.

OPEN YOUR EYES, BELLA. TODAY IS GOING TO BE DULL, DULL...

...DULL

NOW LISTEN UP, PETE...

THIS IS WHAT WE'RE AFTER,

AND IT HAS TO BE TODAY, UNDERSTAND?

SURE THING, MR. ANGELO.

NO MISTAKES.

IT'S GOING TO BE HARD TO DO IT AT THE CASTLE.

I DON'T CARE! DO WHAT YOU HAVE TO DO.

AND DON'T LET *ANYONE* GET IN YOUR WAY.

BUT—

NO BUTS, PETE! AND NO MISTAKES!

YOU WERE *SAYING*?

STOP GLOATING AND GET AFTER HIM!

13

WELL? WHERE IS EVERYBODY? ARE WE SET UP?

RRRRING!

TARGET SIGHTED.

TARGET SIGHTED.

FINALLY!

20

OH, HE'S IN FULL SWING. NOBODY DISTRACTS TEACHERS LIKE *HIM*.

SO WHAT SORT OF STONE WOULD YOU HAVE USED FOR AN ARCHWAY LIKE THAT?

WELL...

HMM ... TELL HIM TO LAY OFF BRIEFLY. WE NEED HIM HERE.

BUT WHAT IF MR CUNNINGHAM SPOTS NAZIM AND BELLA LEAVING?

HE WON'T. GET JOE OUT THERE TO CAUSE A DIVERSION.

IF YOU SAY SO...

SO THE CORNERS ARE ROUNDED TO STOP PEOPLE PLANTING EXPLOSIVES?

EXACTLY! IF YOU WERE LOOKING FOR WEAK POINTS, YOU'D—

BLAP!

22

OKAY. WE'RE AFTER HIM.

JOE'S INTERCEPTED MR CUNNINGHAM. I RECKON WE'VE GOT ABOUT FIVE MINUTES BEFORE HE TAKES HIM BACK TO THE BUS.

THAT SHOULD BE ENOUGH.

YOU REALISE, OF COURSE, THAT WE CAN'T USE JOE AGAIN FOR A WHILE...

I KNOW, I KNOW. BUT THIS IS IMPORTANT.

WE MUST PREDICT THE TARGET'S MOVEMENTS. AND WE CAN'T DO THAT IF WE DON'T KNOW WHAT HE'S DOING.

YOU WANTED TO SEE ME, BOSS?

YEAH, THANKS, PATRICK. WE'LL NEED YOU BACK ON DISTRACTION IN A MINUTE.

BUT FIRST I WANT YOU TO TELL ME WHAT *THIS* IS...

24

26

BOSS?

I'VE GOT ROBBIE AND ANNE HERE. THEY'VE FOUND THE BOOK...

...BUT WE'RE STILL WORKING ON HOW THEY'RE GOING TO STEAL IT.

DO YOU HAVE ANY THEORIES?

WELL, IT'S PRETTY WELL-PROTECTED. ANY ATTEMPT TO STEAL IT WOULD SET OFF AN ALARM.

IF *WE* WERE GOING TO PINCH IT WE'D MAKE A DECOY FIRST, THEN MESS UP THE SECURITY WIRING AND THE CCTV FROM OUTSIDE.

THERE'S ONLY ONE GUARD, WHO WE'D HAVE TO INCAPACITATE SOMEHOW, BUT THAT WOULDN'T BE TOO DIFFICULT.

SO WHAT'S THE PROBLEM, THEN?

30

footer:

34

36

ANY WORD FROM NAZIM?

NOT A WHISPER. HIS PHONE MIGHT BE DEAD OR OUT OF CREDIT.

WELL, HE'S NOT STUPID. THERE'S NO USE IN FOLLOWING THE GUY IF HE CAN'T REPORT BACK.

OKAY, GUYS, THIS IS YOUR STORY. BELLA AND NAZIM HAVE BEEN WITH YOU SINCE MID-DAY. YOU ATE LUNCH AROUND THE SIDE OF THE CASTLE.

AT SOME TIME WILL GOT INTO AN ARGUMENT WITH BELLA AND SHE KICKED HIM IN THE SHINS.

CAN I KICK WILL IN THE SHINS? IT'LL MAKE IT AUTHENTIC!

NO!

KEEP TRYING HIM. WHEN HE ENTERS THE GROUNDS SOMEONE'LL SPOT HIM.

THE TARGETS WILL PROBABLY BOTH CONVERGE ON THE TOWER SOMETIME SOON ANYWAY.

I'LL KICK YOU IN THE SHINS IN A MINUTE!

BUT WHAT IF NAZIM'S IN SERIOUS TROUBLE?

HE'S ONLY BEEN OUT OF CONTACT A SHORT WHILE.

42

44

YOU ARE IN A *LOT* OF TROUBLE, YOUNG LADY!

OH ... OH, I WAS JUST ... AHH...

I'M NOT HAVING ANY OF IT, BELLA. NOT ANY OF IT!

FIRST I GET TOLD THAT TWO PEOPLE WHO LOOK *VERY LIKE* YOU AND NAZIM HAVE BEEN MESSING AROUND OUTSIDE A *PUB*...

THEN I GET TOLD YOU'VE BEEN IN THE CASTLE WITH WILL AND HANNAH AND KATRINA...

...AND *NOW* I FIND YOU HERE, *OUTSIDE THE CASTLE!*

NOW I DON'T KNOW HOW YOU GOT EVERYONE TO *LIE* FOR YOU, BELLA, BUT...

SIR!

49

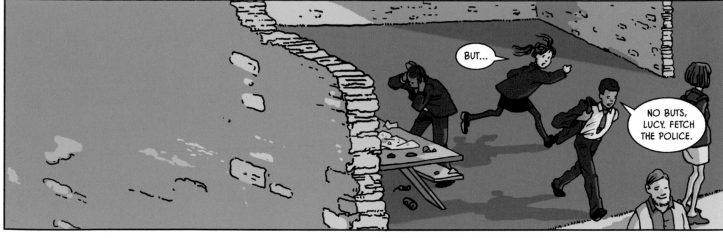

CRASH!

THAT'S WHAT *I* WAS GOING TO SAY...

BUT THEN HE SAID THAT *SIX* OTHER PEOPLE'S DOGS HAVE GONE MISSING...

...ON THE *SAME* STREET.

AHH ... NOW THAT *IS* INTERESTING.

SEND HIM A MESSAGE. TELL HIM WE'LL CALL.

ALL RIGHT! TIME TO GO! EVERYONE ON THE BUS!

HANG ON! HANG ON A SECOND!

YOU KNOW, I JUST REALISED THAT I NEVER THANKED YOU FOR YOUR HELP, EVEN IF IT *WAS* DANGEROUS.

OH, DON'T THANK *ME*...